twenty 23

January

S	M	T	W	T	F	S
1	2	3	4	5	6	7
8	9	10	11	12	13	14
15	16	17	18	19	20	21
22	23	24	25	26	27	28
29	30	31				

February

S	M	T	W	T	F	S
			1	2	3	4
5	6	7	8	9	10	11
12	13	14	15	16	17	18
19	20	21	22	23	24	25
26	27	28				

March

S	M	T	W	T	F	S
			1	2	3	4
5	6	7	8	9	10	11
12	13	14	15	16	17	18
19	20	21	22	23	24	25
26	27	28	29	30	31	

April

S	M	T	W	T	F	S
						1
2	3	4	5	6	7	8
9	10	11	12	13	14	15
16	17	18	19	20	21	22
23	24	25	26	27	28	29
30						

May

S	M	T	W	T	F	S
	1	2	3	4	5	6
7	8	9	10	11	12	13
14	15	16	17	18	19	20
21	22	23	24	25	26	27
28	29	30	31			

June

S	M	T	W	T	F	S
				1	2	3
4	5	6	7	8	9	10
11	12	13	14	15	16	17
18	19	20	21	22	23	24
25	26	27	28	29	30	

July

S	M	T	W	T	F	S
						1
2	3	4	5	6	7	8
9	10	11	12	13	14	15
16	17	18	19	20	21	22
23	24	25	26	27	28	29
30	31					

August

S	M	T	W	T	F	S
		1	2	3	4	5
6	7	8	9	10	11	12
13	14	15	16	17	18	19
20	21	22	23	24	25	26
27	28	29	30	31		

September

S	M	T	W	T	F	S
					1	2
3	4	5	6	7	8	9
10	11	12	13	14	15	16
17	18	19	20	21	22	23
24	25	26	27	28	29	30

October

S	M	T	W	T	F	S
1	2	3	4	5	6	7
8	9	10	11	12	13	14
15	16	17	18	19	20	21
22	23	24	25	26	27	28
29	30	31				

November

S	M	T	W	T	F	S
			1	2	3	4
5	6	7	8	9	10	11
12	13	14	15	16	17	18
19	20	21	22	23	24	25
26	27	28	29	30		

December

S	M	T	W	T	F	S
					1	2
3	4	5	6	7	8	9
10	11	12	13	14	15	16
17	18	19	20	21	22	23
24	25	26	27	28	29	30
31						

IMPORTANT *Dates*

January	February	March
April	May	June
July	August	September
October	November	December

FEDERAL *Holidays* (U.S.)

JANUARY 1, 2023	NEW YEAR'S DAY	SUNDAY
JANUARY 2, 2023	NEW YEAR'S DAY (OBSERVED)	MONDAY
JANUARY 16, 2023	MARTIN LUTHER KING DAY	MONDAY
FEBRUARY 20, 2023	PRESIDENTS' DAY	MONDAY
MAY 29, 2023	MEMORIAL DAY	MONDAY
JUNE 19, 2023	JUNETEENTH	MONDAY
JULY 4, 2023	INDEPENDENCE DAY	TUESDAY
SEPTEMBER 4, 2023	LABOR DAY	MONDAY
OCTOBER 9, 2023	COLUMBUS DAY	MONDAY
NOVEMBER 10, 2023	VETERANS DAY (OBSERVED)	FRIDAY
NOVEMBER 11, 2023	VETERANS DAY	SATURDAY
NOVEMBER 23, 2023	THANKSGIVING DAY	THURSDAY
DECEMBER 25, 2023	CHRISTMAS DAY	MONDAY

Notes:

_____

_____

_____

_____

_____

_____

_____

_____

_____

_____

_____

2023: Year at a Glance

January	February	March

April	May	June

July	August	September

October	November	December

2023: Year at a Glance

January
2023

Monthly Goals

Monthly Snapshot

Top Priorities

TASKS & NOTES

Monthly Wellness Goals

MIND	BODY	SPIRIT
MY HOBBIES, LEARNING, READING, ETC.	MY EATING HABITS, EXERCISE, ETC.	MY PURPOSE & MOTIVATION

ACTION STEPS TO TAKE TO MEET THESE GOALS:

Mind	Body	Spirit

Shit (that kills my joy) to avoid this month:

Shit To Get Done This Month

TO-DO / PROJECT	DUE DATE

Monthly Checklist

(CLEANING TASKS, HOME SERVICES TASKS LIKE
TERMITE OR PEST CONTROL, WORK TASKS, ETC.)

TASKS	MON	TUE	WED	THU	FRI	SAT	SUN
	○	○	○	○	○	○	○
	○	○	○	○	○	○	○
	○	○	○	○	○	○	○
	○	○	○	○	○	○	○
	○	○	○	○	○	○	○
	○	○	○	○	○	○	○
	○	○	○	○	○	○	○
	○	○	○	○	○	○	○
	○	○	○	○	○	○	○
	○	○	○	○	○	○	○
	○	○	○	○	○	○	○
	○	○	○	○	○	○	○
	○	○	○	○	○	○	○
	○	○	○	○	○	○	○
	○	○	○	○	○	○	○
	○	○	○	○	○	○	○
	○	○	○	○	○	○	○
	○	○	○	○	○	○	○
	○	○	○	○	○	○	○
	○	○	○	○	○	○	○
	○	○	○	○	○	○	○
	○	○	○	○	○	○	○
	○	○	○	○	○	○	○
	○	○	○	○	○	○	○
	○	○	○	○	○	○	○
	○	○	○	○	○	○	○
	○	○	○	○	○	○	○
	○	○	○	○	○	○	○
	○	○	○	○	○	○	○
	○	○	○	○	○	○	○

January

	SUN	MON	TUES
	1	2	3
	8	9	10
	15	16	17
	22	23	24
	29	30	31

THIS MONTH'S GOALS:

ACTION LIST:
- ◯ _____
- ◯ _____
- ◯ _____
- ◯ _____
- ◯ _____
- ◯ _____
- ◯ _____
- ◯ _____
- ◯ _____

NOTES:

SHIT TO DO THIS MONTH:

WED	THURS	FRI	SAT
4	5	6	7
11	12	13	14
18	19	20	21
25	26	27	28

February

S	M	T	W	T	F	S
			1	2	3	4
5	6	7	8	9	10	11
12	13	14	15	16	17	18
19	20	21	22	23	24	25
26	27	28				

SORRY. I'M *fresh out of fucks* TODAY.

DAILY Shit To Do

1 SUNDAY	2 MONDAY	3 TUESDAY	4 WEDNESDAY
_____	_____	_____	_____

WATER INTAKE: ○○○○○○○ WATER INTAKE: ○○○○○○○ WATER INTAKE: ○○○○○○○ WATER INTAKE: ○○○○○○○

5 THURSDAY	6 FRIDAY	7 SATURDAY	Notes
_____	_____	_____	_____

WATER INTAKE: ○○○○○○○ WATER INTAKE: ○○○○○○○ WATER INTAKE: ○○○○○○○

Tracker

	M	T	W	TH	F	S	SU
_____	▢	▢	▢	▢	▢	▢	▢
_____	▢	▢	▢	▢	▢	▢	▢
_____	▢	▢	▢	▢	▢	▢	▢
_____	▢	▢	▢	▢	▢	▢	▢

DAILY Shit To Do

8 SUNDAY

WATER INTAKE:

9 MONDAY

WATER INTAKE:

10 TUESDAY

WATER INTAKE:

11 WEDNESDAY

WATER INTAKE:

12 THURSDAY

WATER INTAKE:

13 FRIDAY

WATER INTAKE:

14 SATURDAY

WATER INTAKE:

Notes

Tracker

	M	T	W	TH	F	S	SU

DAILY *Shit To Do*

15 | **SUNDAY**

WATER INTAKE: ○○○○○○○

16 | **MONDAY**

WATER INTAKE: ○○○○○○○

17 | **TUESDAY**

WATER INTAKE: ○○○○○○○

18 | **WEDNESDAY**

WATER INTAKE: ○○○○○○○

19 | **THURSDAY**

WATER INTAKE: ○○○○○○○

20 | **FRIDAY**

WATER INTAKE: ○○○○○○○

21 | **SATURDAY**

WATER INTAKE: ○○○○○○○

Notes

Tracker

		M	T	W	TH	F	S	SU
		☐	☐	☐	☐	☐	☐	☐
		☐	☐	☐	☐	☐	☐	☐
		☐	☐	☐	☐	☐	☐	☐
		☐	☐	☐	☐	☐	☐	☐

DAILY *Shit To Do*

22 SUNDAY

WATER INTAKE: ○○○○○○○

23 MONDAY

WATER INTAKE: ○○○○○○○

24 TUESDAY

WATER INTAKE: ○○○○○○○

25 WEDNESDAY

WATER INTAKE: ○○○○○○○

26 THURSDAY

WATER INTAKE: ○○○○○○○

27 FRIDAY

WATER INTAKE: ○○○○○○○

28 SATURDAY

WATER INTAKE: ○○○○○○○

Notes

Tracker

	M	T	W	TH	F	S	SU
	☐	☐	☐	☐	☐	☐	☐
	☐	☐	☐	☐	☐	☐	☐
	☐	☐	☐	☐	☐	☐	☐
	☐	☐	☐	☐	☐	☐	☐

DAILY *Shit To Do*

29 SUNDAY	30 MONDAY	31 TUESDAY	*Notes*

WATER INTAKE: ○○○○○○○   WATER INTAKE: ○○○○○○○   WATER INTAKE: ○○○○○○○

Tracker

	M	T	W	TH	F	S	SU
	☐	☐	☐	☐	☐	☐	☐
	☐	☐	☐	☐	☐	☐	☐
	☐	☐	☐	☐	☐	☐	☐
	☐	☐	☐	☐	☐	☐	☐

MONTHLY *Check-in*

	1	2	3	4	5	6	7	8	9	10
FAMILY RELATIONSHIPS										
SOCIAL RELATIONSHIPS										
PERSONAL GROWTH										
ROMANTIC RELATIONSHIPS										
WORK/CAREER										
FINANCIAL										
HEALTH/FITNESS										
OVERALL										

1 = Sucked Ass   10 = Fucking Awesome

February
2023

Monthly Goals

Monthly Snapshot

Top Priorities

TASKS & NOTES

Monthly Wellness Goals

MIND
MY HOBBIES, LEARNING, READING, ETC.

BODY
MY EATING HABITS, EXERCISE, ETC.

SPIRIT
MY PURPOSE & MOTIVATION

ACTION STEPS TO TAKE TO MEET THESE GOALS:

Mind

Body

Spirit

Shit (that kills my joy) to avoid this month:

Shit To Get Done This Month

TO-DO / PROJECT	DUE DATE

Monthly Checklist

(CLEANING TASKS, HOME SERVICES TASKS LIKE
TERMITE OR PEST CONTROL, WORK TASKS, ETC.)

TASKS	MON	TUE	WED	THU	FRI	SAT	SUN
	○	○	○	○	○	○	○
	○	○	○	○	○	○	○
	○	○	○	○	○	○	○
	○	○	○	○	○	○	○
	○	○	○	○	○	○	○
	○	○	○	○	○	○	○
	○	○	○	○	○	○	○
	○	○	○	○	○	○	○
	○	○	○	○	○	○	○
	○	○	○	○	○	○	○
	○	○	○	○	○	○	○
	○	○	○	○	○	○	○
	○	○	○	○	○	○	○
	○	○	○	○	○	○	○
	○	○	○	○	○	○	○
	○	○	○	○	○	○	○
	○	○	○	○	○	○	○
	○	○	○	○	○	○	○
	○	○	○	○	○	○	○
	○	○	○	○	○	○	○
	○	○	○	○	○	○	○
	○	○	○	○	○	○	○
	○	○	○	○	○	○	○
	○	○	○	○	○	○	○
	○	○	○	○	○	○	○
	○	○	○	○	○	○	○
	○	○	○	○	○	○	○
	○	○	○	○	○	○	○
	○	○	○	○	○	○	○
	○	○	○	○	○	○	○

February

THIS MONTH'S GOALS:

ACTION LIST:
- ○ _____
- ○ _____
- ○ _____
- ○ _____
- ○ _____
- ○ _____
- ○ _____
- ○ _____
- ○ _____

NOTES:

SUN	MON	TUES
29	30	31
5	6	7
12	13	14
19	20	21
26	27	28

SHIT TO DO THIS MONTH:

WED	THURS	FRI	SAT
1	2	3	4
8	9	10	11
15	16	17	18
22	23	24	25

March

S	M	T	W	T	F	S
			1	2	3	4
5	6	7	8	9	10	11
12	13	14	15	16	17	18
19	20	21	22	23	24	25
26	27	28	29	30	31	

JUST A *Brilliant Badass* BLOWING MINDS DAILY

DAILY Shit To Do

1 WEDNESDAY

WATER INTAKE: ○○○○○○○

2 THURSDAY

WATER INTAKE: ○○○○○○○

3 FRIDAY

WATER INTAKE: ○○○○○○○

4 SATURDAY

WATER INTAKE: ○○○○○○○

5 SUNDAY

WATER INTAKE: ○○○○○○○

6 MONDAY

WATER INTAKE: ○○○○○○○

7 TUESDAY

WATER INTAKE: ○○○○○○○

Notes

Tracker

	M	T	W	TH	F	S	SU

DAILY *Shit To Do*

8 WEDNESDAY

WATER INTAKE: ○○○○○○○

9 THURSDAY

WATER INTAKE: ○○○○○○○

10 FRIDAY

WATER INTAKE: ○○○○○○○

11 SATURDAY

WATER INTAKE: ○○○○○○○

12 SUNDAY

WATER INTAKE: ○○○○○○○

13 MONDAY

WATER INTAKE: ○○○○○○○

14 TUESDAY

WATER INTAKE: ○○○○○○○

Notes

Tracker

	M	T	W	TH	F	S	SU
	☐	☐	☐	☐	☐	☐	☐
	☐	☐	☐	☐	☐	☐	☐
	☐	☐	☐	☐	☐	☐	☐
	☐	☐	☐	☐	☐	☐	☐

DAILY Shit To Do

15 WEDNESDAY

WATER INTAKE: ○○○○○○○

16 THURSDAY

WATER INTAKE: ○○○○○○○

17 FRIDAY

WATER INTAKE: ○○○○○○○

18 SATURDAY

WATER INTAKE: ○○○○○○○

19 SUNDAY

WATER INTAKE: ○○○○○○○

20 MONDAY

WATER INTAKE: ○○○○○○○

21 TUESDAY

WATER INTAKE: ○○○○○○○

Notes

Tracker

		M	T	W	TH	F	S	SU
		☐	☐	☐	☐	☐	☐	☐
		☐	☐	☐	☐	☐	☐	☐
		☐	☐	☐	☐	☐	☐	☐
		☐	☐	☐	☐	☐	☐	☐

DAILY *Shit To Do*

22 WEDNESDAY

WATER INTAKE: ◇◇◇◇◇◇◇

23 THURSDAY

WATER INTAKE: ◇◇◇◇◇◇◇

24 FRIDAY

WATER INTAKE: ◇◇◇◇◇◇◇

25 SATURDAY

WATER INTAKE: ◇◇◇◇◇◇◇

26 SUNDAY

WATER INTAKE: ◇◇◇◇◇◇◇

27 MONDAY

WATER INTAKE: ◇◇◇◇◇◇◇

28 TUESDAY

WATER INTAKE: ◇◇◇◇◇◇◇

Notes

Tracker

	M	T	W	TH	F	S	SU
	☐	☐	☐	☐	☐	☐	☐
	☐	☐	☐	☐	☐	☐	☐
	☐	☐	☐	☐	☐	☐	☐
	☐	☐	☐	☐	☐	☐	☐

MONTHLY *Check-in*

	1	2	3	4	5	6	7	8	9	10
FAMILY RELATIONSHIPS										
SOCIAL RELATIONSHIPS										
PERSONAL GROWTH										
ROMANTIC RELATIONSHIPS										
WORK/CAREER										
FINANCIAL										
HEALTH/FITNESS										
OVERALL										

1 = Sucked Ass   10 = Fucking Awesome

March

March

2023

Monthly Goals

Monthly Snapshot

Top Priorities

TASKS & NOTES

Monthly Wellness Goals

MIND	BODY	SPIRIT
MY HOBBIES, LEARNING, READING, ETC.	MY EATING HABITS, EXERCISE, ETC.	MY PURPOSE & MOTIVATION

ACTION STEPS TO TAKE TO MEET THESE GOALS:

Mind	Body	Spirit

Shit (that kills my joy) to avoid this month:

Shit To Get Done This Month

TO-DO / PROJECT	DUE DATE

Monthly Checklist

(CLEANING TASKS, HOME SERVICES TASKS LIKE TERMITE OR PEST CONTROL, WORK TASKS, ETC.)

TASKS	MON	TUE	WED	THU	FRI	SAT	SUN
	○	○	○	○	○	○	○
	○	○	○	○	○	○	○
	○	○	○	○	○	○	○
	○	○	○	○	○	○	○
	○	○	○	○	○	○	○
	○	○	○	○	○	○	○
	○	○	○	○	○	○	○
	○	○	○	○	○	○	○
	○	○	○	○	○	○	○
	○	○	○	○	○	○	○
	○	○	○	○	○	○	○
	○	○	○	○	○	○	○
	○	○	○	○	○	○	○
	○	○	○	○	○	○	○
	○	○	○	○	○	○	○
	○	○	○	○	○	○	○
	○	○	○	○	○	○	○
	○	○	○	○	○	○	○
	○	○	○	○	○	○	○
	○	○	○	○	○	○	○
	○	○	○	○	○	○	○
	○	○	○	○	○	○	○
	○	○	○	○	○	○	○
	○	○	○	○	○	○	○
	○	○	○	○	○	○	○
	○	○	○	○	○	○	○
	○	○	○	○	○	○	○
	○	○	○	○	○	○	○
	○	○	○	○	○	○	○
	○	○	○	○	○	○	○

March

	SUN	MON	TUES
	26	27	28
	5	6	7
	12	13	14
	19	20	21
	26	27	28

THIS MONTH'S GOALS:

ACTION LIST:
- ◯ _____
- ◯ _____
- ◯ _____
- ◯ _____
- ◯ _____
- ◯ _____
- ◯ _____
- ◯ _____
- ◯ _____

NOTES:

SHIT TO DO THIS MONTH:

WED	THURS	FRI	SAT
1	2	3	4
8	9	10	11
15	16	17	18
22	23	24	25
29	30	31	April

April

S	M	T	W	T	F	S
						1
2	3	4	5	6	7	8
9	10	11	12	13	14	15
16	17	18	19	20	21	22
23	24	25	26	27	28	29
30						

RISE & FUCKING GRIND
sunshine

DAILY Shit To Do

1 WEDNESDAY

_____
_____
_____
_____
_____
_____
_____
_____
_____
_____
_____
_____
_____

WATER INTAKE: ○○○○○○○

2 THURSDAY

_____
_____
_____
_____
_____
_____
_____
_____
_____
_____
_____
_____
_____

WATER INTAKE: ○○○○○○○

3 FRIDAY

_____
_____
_____
_____
_____
_____
_____
_____
_____
_____
_____
_____
_____

WATER INTAKE: ○○○○○○○

4 SATURDAY

_____
_____
_____
_____
_____
_____
_____
_____
_____
_____
_____
_____
_____

WATER INTAKE: ○○○○○○○

5 SUNDAY

_____
_____
_____
_____
_____
_____
_____
_____
_____
_____
_____
_____
_____

WATER INTAKE: ○○○○○○○

6 MONDAY

_____
_____
_____
_____
_____
_____
_____
_____
_____
_____
_____
_____
_____

WATER INTAKE: ○○○○○○○

7 TUESDAY

_____
_____
_____
_____
_____
_____
_____
_____
_____
_____
_____
_____
_____

WATER INTAKE: ○○○○○○○

Notes

_____
_____
_____
_____
_____
_____
_____
_____
_____
_____
_____
_____
_____
_____
_____
_____

Tracker

		M	T	W	TH	F	S	SU
_____		☐	☐	☐	☐	☐	☐	☐
_____		☐	☐	☐	☐	☐	☐	☐
_____		☐	☐	☐	☐	☐	☐	☐
_____		☐	☐	☐	☐	☐	☐	☐

DAILY *Shit To Do*

8 WEDNESDAY

WATER INTAKE: ⬡⬡⬡⬡⬡⬡⬡

9 THURSDAY

WATER INTAKE: ⬡⬡⬡⬡⬡⬡⬡

10 FRIDAY

WATER INTAKE: ⬡⬡⬡⬡⬡⬡⬡

11 SATURDAY

WATER INTAKE: ⬡⬡⬡⬡⬡⬡⬡

12 SUNDAY

WATER INTAKE: ⬡⬡⬡⬡⬡⬡⬡

13 MONDAY

WATER INTAKE: ⬡⬡⬡⬡⬡⬡⬡

14 TUESDAY

WATER INTAKE: ⬡⬡⬡⬡⬡⬡⬡

Notes

Tracker

	M	T	W	TH	F	S	SU

DAILY Shit To Do

15 WEDNESDAY

_____
_____
_____
_____
_____
_____
_____
_____
_____
_____
_____
_____
_____
_____
_____

WATER INTAKE: ⬡⬡⬡⬡⬡⬡⬡

16 THURSDAY

_____
_____
_____
_____
_____
_____
_____
_____
_____
_____
_____
_____
_____
_____
_____

WATER INTAKE: ⬡⬡⬡⬡⬡⬡⬡

17 FRIDAY

_____
_____
_____
_____
_____
_____
_____
_____
_____
_____
_____
_____
_____
_____
_____

WATER INTAKE: ⬡⬡⬡⬡⬡⬡⬡

18 SATURDAY

_____
_____
_____
_____
_____
_____
_____
_____
_____
_____
_____
_____
_____
_____
_____

WATER INTAKE: ⬡⬡⬡⬡⬡⬡⬡

19 SUNDAY

_____
_____
_____
_____
_____
_____
_____
_____
_____
_____
_____
_____
_____
_____
_____

WATER INTAKE: ⬡⬡⬡⬡⬡⬡⬡

20 MONDAY

_____
_____
_____
_____
_____
_____
_____
_____
_____
_____
_____
_____
_____
_____
_____

WATER INTAKE: ⬡⬡⬡⬡⬡⬡⬡

21 TUESDAY

_____
_____
_____
_____
_____
_____
_____
_____
_____
_____
_____
_____
_____
_____
_____

WATER INTAKE: ⬡⬡⬡⬡⬡⬡⬡

Notes

_____
_____
_____
_____
_____
_____
_____
_____
_____
_____
_____
_____
_____
_____
_____
_____
_____
_____

Tracker

					M	T	W	TH	F	S	SU
_____					☐	☐	☐	☐	☐	☐	☐
_____					☐	☐	☐	☐	☐	☐	☐
_____					☐	☐	☐	☐	☐	☐	☐
_____					☐	☐	☐	☐	☐	☐	☐

DAILY *Shit To Do*

22 **WEDNESDAY**	23 **THURSDAY**	24 **FRIDAY**	25 **SATURDAY**

WATER INTAKE: ○○○○○○○   WATER INTAKE: ○○○○○○○   WATER INTAKE: ○○○○○○○   WATER INTAKE: ○○○○○○○

26 **SUNDAY**	27 **MONDAY**	28 **TUESDAY**	*Notes*

WATER INTAKE: ○○○○○○○   WATER INTAKE: ○○○○○○○   WATER INTAKE: ○○○○○○○

Tracker

	M	T	W	TH	F	S	SU
	☐	☐	☐	☐	☐	☐	☐
	☐	☐	☐	☐	☐	☐	☐
	☐	☐	☐	☐	☐	☐	☐
	☐	☐	☐	☐	☐	☐	☐

DAILY Shit To Do

29 WEDNESDAY
_____
_____
_____
_____
_____
_____
_____
_____
_____
_____
_____
_____
_____
_____

WATER INTAKE: ○○○○○○○

30 THURSDAY
_____
_____
_____
_____
_____
_____
_____
_____
_____
_____
_____
_____
_____
_____

WATER INTAKE: ○○○○○○○

31 FRIDAY
_____
_____
_____
_____
_____
_____
_____
_____
_____
_____
_____
_____
_____
_____

WATER INTAKE: ○○○○○○○

Notes
_____
_____
_____
_____
_____
_____
_____
_____
_____
_____
_____
_____
_____
_____
_____
_____
_____

Tracker

	M	T	W	TH	F	S	SU
_____							
_____							
_____							
_____							

MONTHLY Check-in

	1	2	3	4	5	6	7	8	9	10
FAMILY RELATIONSHIPS										
SOCIAL RELATIONSHIPS										
PERSONAL GROWTH										
ROMANTIC RELATIONSHIPS										
WORK/CAREER										
FINANCIAL										
HEALTH/FITNESS										
OVERALL										

1 = Sucked Ass   10 = Fucking Awesome

April

2023

Monthly Goals

Monthly Snapshot

Top Priorities

TASKS & NOTES

Monthly Wellness Goals

MIND
MY HOBBIES, LEARNING, READING, ETC.

BODY
MY EATING HABITS, EXERCISE, ETC.

SPIRIT
MY PURPOSE & MOTIVATION

ACTION STEPS TO TAKE TO MEET THESE GOALS:

Mind

Body

Spirit

Shit (that kills my joy) to avoid this month:

Shit To Get Done This Month

TO-DO / PROJECT	DUE DATE

Monthly Checklist

(CLEANING TASKS, HOME SERVICES TASKS LIKE
TERMITE OR PEST CONTROL, WORK TASKS, ETC.)

TASKS	MON	TUE	WED	THU	FRI	SAT	SUN
	○	○	○	○	○	○	○
	○	○	○	○	○	○	○
	○	○	○	○	○	○	○
	○	○	○	○	○	○	○
	○	○	○	○	○	○	○
	○	○	○	○	○	○	○
	○	○	○	○	○	○	○
	○	○	○	○	○	○	○
	○	○	○	○	○	○	○
	○	○	○	○	○	○	○
	○	○	○	○	○	○	○
	○	○	○	○	○	○	○
	○	○	○	○	○	○	○
	○	○	○	○	○	○	○
	○	○	○	○	○	○	○
	○	○	○	○	○	○	○
	○	○	○	○	○	○	○
	○	○	○	○	○	○	○
	○	○	○	○	○	○	○
	○	○	○	○	○	○	○
	○	○	○	○	○	○	○
	○	○	○	○	○	○	○
	○	○	○	○	○	○	○
	○	○	○	○	○	○	○
	○	○	○	○	○	○	○
	○	○	○	○	○	○	○
	○	○	○	○	○	○	○
	○	○	○	○	○	○	○
	○	○	○	○	○	○	○
	○	○	○	○	○	○	○
	○	○	○	○	○	○	○

April

THIS MONTH'S GOALS:

ACTION LIST:
- ○ _____
- ○ _____
- ○ _____
- ○ _____
- ○ _____
- ○ _____
- ○ _____
- ○ _____
- ○ _____

NOTES:

SUN	MON	TUES
26	27	28
2	3	4
9	10	11
16	17	18
23	24	25
30	SHIT TO DO THIS MONTH:	

WED	THURS	FRI	SAT
29	30	31	1
5	6	7	8
12	13	14	15
19	20	21	22
26	27	28	29

Fuck what they think.

May

S	M	T	W	T	F	S
	1	2	3	4	5	6
7	8	9	10	11	12	13
14	15	16	17	18	19	20
21	22	23	24	25	26	27
28	29	30	31			

DAILY Shit To Do

1 SATURDAY	2 SUNDAY	3 MONDAY	4 TUESDAY
WATER INTAKE: ○○○○○○○	WATER INTAKE: ○○○○○○○	WATER INTAKE: ○○○○○○○	WATER INTAKE: ○○○○○○○

5 WEDNESDAY	6 THURSDAY	7 FRIDAY	Notes
WATER INTAKE: ○○○○○○○	WATER INTAKE: ○○○○○○○	WATER INTAKE: ○○○○○○○	

Tracker

	M	T	W	TH	F	S	SU
	☐	☐	☐	☐	☐	☐	☐
	☐	☐	☐	☐	☐	☐	☐
	☐	☐	☐	☐	☐	☐	☐
	☐	☐	☐	☐	☐	☐	☐

DAILY *Shit To Do*

8 SATURDAY	**9** SUNDAY	**10** MONDAY	**11** TUESDAY
WATER INTAKE: ○○○○○○○	WATER INTAKE: ○○○○○○○	WATER INTAKE: ○○○○○○○	WATER INTAKE: ○○○○○○○

12 WEDNESDAY	**13** THURSDAY	**14** FRIDAY	*Notes*
WATER INTAKE: ○○○○○○○	WATER INTAKE: ○○○○○○○	WATER INTAKE: ○○○○○○○	

Tracker

	M	T	W	TH	F	S	SU
	☐	☐	☐	☐	☐	☐	☐
	☐	☐	☐	☐	☐	☐	☐
	☐	☐	☐	☐	☐	☐	☐
	☐	☐	☐	☐	☐	☐	☐

DAILY *Shit To Do*

15 SATURDAY

_____
_____
_____
_____
_____
_____
_____
_____
_____
_____
_____
_____
_____
_____
_____
_____
_____

WATER INTAKE: ○○○○○○○

16 SUNDAY

_____
_____
_____
_____
_____
_____
_____
_____
_____
_____
_____
_____
_____
_____
_____
_____
_____

WATER INTAKE: ○○○○○○○

17 MONDAY

_____
_____
_____
_____
_____
_____
_____
_____
_____
_____
_____
_____
_____
_____
_____
_____
_____

WATER INTAKE: ○○○○○○○

18 TUESDAY

_____
_____
_____
_____
_____
_____
_____
_____
_____
_____
_____
_____
_____
_____
_____
_____
_____

WATER INTAKE: ○○○○○○○

19 WEDNESDAY

_____
_____
_____
_____
_____
_____
_____
_____
_____
_____
_____
_____
_____
_____
_____
_____
_____

WATER INTAKE: ○○○○○○○

20 THURSDAY

_____
_____
_____
_____
_____
_____
_____
_____
_____
_____
_____
_____
_____
_____
_____
_____
_____

WATER INTAKE: ○○○○○○○

21 FRIDAY

_____
_____
_____
_____
_____
_____
_____
_____
_____
_____
_____
_____
_____
_____
_____
_____
_____

WATER INTAKE: ○○○○○○○

Notes

_____
_____
_____
_____
_____
_____
_____
_____
_____
_____
_____
_____
_____
_____
_____
_____
_____
_____
_____
_____
_____
_____
_____

Tracker

		M	T	W	TH	F	S	SU
_____		☐	☐	☐	☐	☐	☐	☐
_____		☐	☐	☐	☐	☐	☐	☐
_____		☐	☐	☐	☐	☐	☐	☐
_____		☐	☐	☐	☐	☐	☐	☐

DAILY Shit To Do

22 SATURDAY

WATER INTAKE: ○○○○○○○

23 SUNDAY

WATER INTAKE: ○○○○○○○

24 MONDAY

WATER INTAKE: ○○○○○○○

25 TUESDAY

WATER INTAKE: ○○○○○○○

26 WEDNESDAY

WATER INTAKE: ○○○○○○○

27 THURSDAY

WATER INTAKE: ○○○○○○○

28 FRIDAY

WATER INTAKE: ○○○○○○○

Notes

Tracker

		M	T	W	TH	F	S	SU
		☐	☐	☐	☐	☐	☐	☐
		☐	☐	☐	☐	☐	☐	☐
		☐	☐	☐	☐	☐	☐	☐
		☐	☐	☐	☐	☐	☐	☐

DAILY Shit To Do

29 SATURDAY	30 SUNDAY	Notes
_____	_____	_____
_____	_____	_____
_____	_____	_____
_____	_____	_____
_____	_____	_____
_____	_____	_____

WATER INTAKE: ◇◇◇◇◇◇◇◇   WATER INTAKE: ◇◇◇◇◇◇◇◇

Tracker

	M	T	W	TH	F	S	SU
_____	☐	☐	☐	☐	☐	☐	☐
_____	☐	☐	☐	☐	☐	☐	☐
_____	☐	☐	☐	☐	☐	☐	☐
_____	☐	☐	☐	☐	☐	☐	☐

MONTHLY Check-in

	1	2	3	4	5	6	7	8	9	10
FAMILY RELATIONSHIPS										
SOCIAL RELATIONSHIPS										
PERSONAL GROWTH										
ROMANTIC RELATIONSHIPS										
WORK/CAREER										
FINANCIAL										
HEALTH/FITNESS										
OVERALL										

1 = Sucked Ass   10 = Fucking Awesome

May
2023

Monthly Goals

Monthly Snapshot

Top Priorities

TASKS & NOTES

Monthly Wellness Goals

MIND
MY HOBBIES, LEARNING,
READING, ETC.

BODY
MY EATING HABITS,
EXERCISE, ETC.

SPIRIT
MY PURPOSE
& MOTIVATION

ACTION STEPS TO TAKE TO MEET THESE GOALS:

Mind

Body

Spirit

Shit (that kills my joy) to avoid this month:

Shit To Get Done This Month

TO-DO / PROJECT	DUE DATE

Monthly Checklist

(CLEANING TASKS, HOME SERVICES TASKS LIKE
TERMITE OR PEST CONTROL, WORK TASKS, ETC.)

TASKS	MON	TUE	WED	THU	FRI	SAT	SUN
	○	○	○	○	○	○	○
	○	○	○	○	○	○	○
	○	○	○	○	○	○	○
	○	○	○	○	○	○	○
	○	○	○	○	○	○	○
	○	○	○	○	○	○	○
	○	○	○	○	○	○	○
	○	○	○	○	○	○	○
	○	○	○	○	○	○	○
	○	○	○	○	○	○	○
	○	○	○	○	○	○	○
	○	○	○	○	○	○	○
	○	○	○	○	○	○	○
	○	○	○	○	○	○	○
	○	○	○	○	○	○	○
	○	○	○	○	○	○	○
	○	○	○	○	○	○	○
	○	○	○	○	○	○	○
	○	○	○	○	○	○	○
	○	○	○	○	○	○	○
	○	○	○	○	○	○	○
	○	○	○	○	○	○	○
	○	○	○	○	○	○	○
	○	○	○	○	○	○	○
	○	○	○	○	○	○	○
	○	○	○	○	○	○	○
	○	○	○	○	○	○	○
	○	○	○	○	○	○	○
	○	○	○	○	○	○	○
	○	○	○	○	○	○	○

May

THIS MONTH'S GOALS:

SUN	MON	TUES
30	1	2
7	8	9
14	15	16
21	22	23
28	29	30

ACTION LIST:
- ○ _____
- ○ _____
- ○ _____
- ○ _____
- ○ _____
- ○ _____
- ○ _____
- ○ _____
- ○ _____

NOTES:

SHIT TO DO THIS MONTH:

WED	THURS	FRI	SAT
3	4	5	6
10	11	12	13
17	18	19	20
24	25	26	27
31			

June

S	M	T	W	T	F	S
				1	2	3
4	5	6	7	8	9	10
11	12	13	14	15	16	17
18	19	20	21	22	23	24
25	26	27	28	29	30	

I'M A LOVELY LITTLE RAY OF

 fucking darkness

DAILY Shit To Do

1 MONDAY

WATER INTAKE: ○○○○○○○

2 TUESDAY

WATER INTAKE: ○○○○○○○

3 WEDNESDAY

WATER INTAKE: ○○○○○○○

4 THURSDAY

WATER INTAKE: ○○○○○○○

5 FRIDAY

WATER INTAKE: ○○○○○○○

6 SATURDAY

WATER INTAKE: ○○○○○○○

7 SUNDAY

WATER INTAKE: ○○○○○○○

Notes

Tracker

	M	T	W	TH	F	S	SU

DAILY Shit To Do

8 MONDAY

WATER
INTAKE: ○○○○○○○

9 TUESDAY

WATER
INTAKE: ○○○○○○○

10 WEDNESDAY

WATER
INTAKE: ○○○○○○○

11 THURSDAY

WATER
INTAKE: ○○○○○○○

12 FRIDAY

WATER
INTAKE: ○○○○○○○

13 SATURDAY

WATER
INTAKE: ○○○○○○○

14 SUNDAY

WATER
INTAKE: ○○○○○○○

Notes

Tracker

		M	T	W	TH	F	S	SU
		☐	☐	☐	☐	☐	☐	☐
		☐	☐	☐	☐	☐	☐	☐
		☐	☐	☐	☐	☐	☐	☐
		☐	☐	☐	☐	☐	☐	☐

DAILY Shit To Do

15 MONDAY

16 TUESDAY

17 WEDNESDAY

18 THURSDAY

WATER INTAKE: ⬡⬡⬡⬡⬡⬡⬡

19 FRIDAY

20 SATURDAY

21 SUNDAY

Notes

WATER INTAKE: ⬡⬡⬡⬡⬡⬡⬡

Tracker

		M	T	W	TH	F	S	SU

DAILY *Shit To Do*

22 **MONDAY**	23 **TUESDAY**	24 **WEDNESDAY**	25 **THURSDAY**
WATER INTAKE: ⬡⬡⬡⬡⬡⬡⬡	WATER INTAKE: ⬡⬡⬡⬡⬡⬡⬡	WATER INTAKE: ⬡⬡⬡⬡⬡⬡⬡	WATER INTAKE: ⬡⬡⬡⬡⬡⬡⬡

26 **FRIDAY**	27 **SATURDAY**	28 **SUNDAY**	*Notes*
WATER INTAKE: ⬡⬡⬡⬡⬡⬡⬡	WATER INTAKE: ⬡⬡⬡⬡⬡⬡⬡	WATER INTAKE: ⬡⬡⬡⬡⬡⬡⬡	

Tracker

	M	T	W	TH	F	S	SU
	☐	☐	☐	☐	☐	☐	☐
	☐	☐	☐	☐	☐	☐	☐
	☐	☐	☐	☐	☐	☐	☐
	☐	☐	☐	☐	☐	☐	☐

DAILY Shit To Do

29 MONDAY	30 TUESDAY	31 WEDNESDAY	Notes
_____	_____	_____	_____
_____	_____	_____	_____
_____	_____	_____	_____
_____	_____	_____	_____
_____	_____	_____	_____
_____	_____	_____	_____
_____	_____	_____	_____
_____	_____	_____	_____
_____	_____	_____	_____
_____	_____	_____	_____
_____	_____	_____	_____
_____	_____	_____	_____
_____	_____	_____	_____
WATER INTAKE: ○○○○○○○	WATER INTAKE: ○○○○○○○	WATER INTAKE: ○○○○○○○	

Tracker

	M	T	W	TH	F	S	SU
_____							
_____							
_____							
_____							

MONTHLY Check-in

	1	2	3	4	5	6	7	8	9	10
FAMILY RELATIONSHIPS										
SOCIAL RELATIONSHIPS										
PERSONAL GROWTH										
ROMANTIC RELATIONSHIPS										
WORK/CAREER										
FINANCIAL										
HEALTH/FITNESS										
OVERALL										

1 = Sucked Ass   10 = Fucking Awesome

June
2023

Monthly Goals

Monthly Snapshot

Top Priorities

TASKS & NOTES

Monthly Wellness Goals

MIND
MY HOBBIES, LEARNING, READING, ETC.

BODY
MY EATING HABITS, EXERCISE, ETC.

SPIRIT
MY PURPOSE & MOTIVATION

ACTION STEPS TO TAKE TO MEET THESE GOALS:

Mind

Body

Spirit

Shit (that kills my joy) to avoid this month:

Shit To Get Done This Month

TO-DO / PROJECT	DUE DATE

Monthly Checklist

(CLEANING TASKS, HOME SERVICES TASKS LIKE
TERMITE OR PEST CONTROL, WORK TASKS, ETC.)

TASKS	MON	TUE	WED	THU	FRI	SAT	SUN
	◯	◯	◯	◯	◯	◯	◯
	◯	◯	◯	◯	◯	◯	◯
	◯	◯	◯	◯	◯	◯	◯
	◯	◯	◯	◯	◯	◯	◯
	◯	◯	◯	◯	◯	◯	◯
	◯	◯	◯	◯	◯	◯	◯
	◯	◯	◯	◯	◯	◯	◯
	◯	◯	◯	◯	◯	◯	◯
	◯	◯	◯	◯	◯	◯	◯
	◯	◯	◯	◯	◯	◯	◯
	◯	◯	◯	◯	◯	◯	◯
	◯	◯	◯	◯	◯	◯	◯
	◯	◯	◯	◯	◯	◯	◯
	◯	◯	◯	◯	◯	◯	◯
	◯	◯	◯	◯	◯	◯	◯
	◯	◯	◯	◯	◯	◯	◯
	◯	◯	◯	◯	◯	◯	◯
	◯	◯	◯	◯	◯	◯	◯
	◯	◯	◯	◯	◯	◯	◯
	◯	◯	◯	◯	◯	◯	◯
	◯	◯	◯	◯	◯	◯	◯
	◯	◯	◯	◯	◯	◯	◯
	◯	◯	◯	◯	◯	◯	◯
	◯	◯	◯	◯	◯	◯	◯
	◯	◯	◯	◯	◯	◯	◯
	◯	◯	◯	◯	◯	◯	◯
	◯	◯	◯	◯	◯	◯	◯
	◯	◯	◯	◯	◯	◯	◯
	◯	◯	◯	◯	◯	◯	◯
	◯	◯	◯	◯	◯	◯	◯
	◯	◯	◯	◯	◯	◯	◯

June

SUN	MON	TUES
28	29	30
4	5	6
11	12	13
18	19	20
25	26	27

THIS MONTH'S GOALS:

ACTION LIST:
- ○
- ○
- ○
- ○
- ○
- ○
- ○
- ○
- ○

NOTES:

SHIT TO DO THIS MONTH:

WED	THURS	FRI	SAT
31	1	2	3
7	8	9	10
14	15	16	17
21	22	23	24
28	29	30	

July

S	M	T	W	T	F	S
						1
2	3	4	5	6	7	8
9	10	11	12	13	14	15
16	17	18	19	20	21	22
23	24	25	26	27	28	29
30	31					

◆ **I'M NOT A** *bitch* ◆
I'M JUST A TELLER OF *unpopular truths*

DAILY *Shit To Do*

1 THURSDAY	**2** FRIDAY	**3** SATURDAY	**4** SUNDAY

WATER INTAKE: ⬡⬡⬡⬡⬡⬡⬡ (×4)

5 MONDAY	**6** TUESDAY	**7** WEDNESDAY	*Notes*

WATER INTAKE: ⬡⬡⬡⬡⬡⬡⬡ (×3)

Tracker

	M	T	W	TH	F	S	SU
	▢	▢	▢	▢	▢	▢	▢
	▢	▢	▢	▢	▢	▢	▢
	▢	▢	▢	▢	▢	▢	▢
	▢	▢	▢	▢	▢	▢	▢

DAILY Shit To Do

8 THURSDAY

WATER INTAKE: ○○○○○○○

9 FRIDAY

WATER INTAKE: ○○○○○○○

10 SATURDAY

WATER INTAKE: ○○○○○○○

11 SUNDAY

WATER INTAKE: ○○○○○○○

12 MONDAY

WATER INTAKE: ○○○○○○○

13 TUESDAY

WATER INTAKE: ○○○○○○○

14 WEDNESDAY

WATER INTAKE: ○○○○○○○

Notes

Tracker

	M	T	W	TH	F	S	SU

DAILY Shit To Do

15 THURSDAY

WATER INTAKE: ○○○○○○○

16 FRIDAY

WATER INTAKE: ○○○○○○○

17 SATURDAY

WATER INTAKE: ○○○○○○○

18 SUNDAY

WATER INTAKE: ○○○○○○○

19 MONDAY

WATER INTAKE: ○○○○○○○

20 TUESDAY

WATER INTAKE: ○○○○○○○

21 WEDNESDAY

WATER INTAKE: ○○○○○○○

Notes

Tracker

	M	T	W	TH	F	S	SU

DAILY *Shit To Do*

22 THURSDAY

WATER INTAKE: ○○○○○○○

23 FRIDAY

WATER INTAKE: ○○○○○○○

24 SATURDAY

WATER INTAKE: ○○○○○○○

25 SUNDAY

WATER INTAKE: ○○○○○○○

26 MONDAY

WATER INTAKE: ○○○○○○○

27 TUESDAY

WATER INTAKE: ○○○○○○○

28 WEDNESDAY

WATER INTAKE: ○○○○○○○

Notes

Tracker

	M	T	W	TH	F	S	SU
	☐	☐	☐	☐	☐	☐	☐
	☐	☐	☐	☐	☐	☐	☐
	☐	☐	☐	☐	☐	☐	☐
	☐	☐	☐	☐	☐	☐	☐

DAILY Shit To Do

29 **THURSDAY**	30 **FRIDAY**	*Notes*

WATER INTAKE: ○○○○○○○○ WATER INTAKE: ○○○○○○○○

Tracker   **M T W TH F S SU**

_____ ☐☐☐☐☐☐☐

_____ ☐☐☐☐☐☐☐

_____ ☐☐☐☐☐☐☐

_____ ☐☐☐☐☐☐☐

MONTHLY Check-in

	1	2	3	4	5	6	7	8	9	10
FAMILY RELATIONSHIPS										
SOCIAL RELATIONSHIPS										
PERSONAL GROWTH										
ROMANTIC RELATIONSHIPS										
WORK/CAREER										
FINANCIAL										
HEALTH/FITNESS										
OVERALL										

1 = Sucked Ass   10 = Fucking Awesome

July

2023

Monthly Goals

Monthly Snapshot

Top Priorities

TASKS & NOTES

Monthly Wellness Goals

MIND	BODY	SPIRIT
MY HOBBIES, LEARNING, READING, ETC.	MY EATING HABITS, EXERCISE, ETC.	MY PURPOSE & MOTIVATION

ACTION STEPS TO TAKE TO MEET THESE GOALS:

Mind	Body	Spirit

Shit (that kills my joy) to avoid this month:

Shit To Get Done This Month

TO-DO / PROJECT	DUE DATE

Monthly Checklist

(CLEANING TASKS, HOME SERVICES TASKS LIKE
TERMITE OR PEST CONTROL, WORK TASKS, ETC.)

TASKS	MON	TUE	WED	THU	FRI	SAT	SUN
	○	○	○	○	○	○	○
	○	○	○	○	○	○	○
	○	○	○	○	○	○	○
	○	○	○	○	○	○	○
	○	○	○	○	○	○	○
	○	○	○	○	○	○	○
	○	○	○	○	○	○	○
	○	○	○	○	○	○	○
	○	○	○	○	○	○	○
	○	○	○	○	○	○	○
	○	○	○	○	○	○	○
	○	○	○	○	○	○	○
	○	○	○	○	○	○	○
	○	○	○	○	○	○	○
	○	○	○	○	○	○	○
	○	○	○	○	○	○	○
	○	○	○	○	○	○	○
	○	○	○	○	○	○	○
	○	○	○	○	○	○	○
	○	○	○	○	○	○	○
	○	○	○	○	○	○	○
	○	○	○	○	○	○	○
	○	○	○	○	○	○	○
	○	○	○	○	○	○	○
	○	○	○	○	○	○	○
	○	○	○	○	○	○	○
	○	○	○	○	○	○	○
	○	○	○	○	○	○	○
	○	○	○	○	○	○	○
	○	○	○	○	○	○	○

July

	SUN	MON	TUES
THIS MONTH'S GOALS:	25	26	27
	2	3	4
ACTION LIST:	9	10	11
	16	17	18
NOTES:	23	24	25
	30	31	SHIT TO DO THIS MONTH:

WED	THURS	FRI	SAT
28	29	30	1
5	6	7	8
12	13	14	15
19	20	21	22
26	27	28	29

Let that shit go

August

S	M	T	W	T	F	S
		1	2	3	4	5
6	7	8	9	10	11	12
13	14	15	16	17	18	19
20	21	22	23	24	25	26
27	28	29	30	31		

DAILY Shit To Do

1 SATURDAY

_____
_____
_____
_____
_____
_____
_____
_____
_____
_____
_____
_____
_____
_____

WATER INTAKE: ⬡⬡⬡⬡⬡⬡⬡

2 SUNDAY

_____
_____
_____
_____
_____
_____
_____
_____
_____
_____
_____
_____
_____
_____

WATER INTAKE: ⬡⬡⬡⬡⬡⬡⬡

3 MONDAY

_____
_____
_____
_____
_____
_____
_____
_____
_____
_____
_____
_____
_____
_____

WATER INTAKE: ⬡⬡⬡⬡⬡⬡⬡

4 TUESDAY

_____
_____
_____
_____
_____
_____
_____
_____
_____
_____
_____
_____
_____
_____

WATER INTAKE: ⬡⬡⬡⬡⬡⬡⬡

5 WEDNESDAY

_____
_____
_____
_____
_____
_____
_____
_____
_____
_____
_____
_____
_____

WATER INTAKE: ⬡⬡⬡⬡⬡⬡⬡

6 THURSDAY

_____
_____
_____
_____
_____
_____
_____
_____
_____
_____
_____
_____
_____

WATER INTAKE: ⬡⬡⬡⬡⬡⬡⬡

7 FRIDAY

_____
_____
_____
_____
_____
_____
_____
_____
_____
_____
_____
_____
_____

WATER INTAKE: ⬡⬡⬡⬡⬡⬡⬡

Notes

_____
_____
_____
_____
_____
_____
_____
_____
_____
_____
_____
_____
_____
_____
_____
_____
_____
_____
_____
_____

Tracker

	M	T	W	TH	F	S	SU
_____	☐	☐	☐	☐	☐	☐	☐
_____	☐	☐	☐	☐	☐	☐	☐
_____	☐	☐	☐	☐	☐	☐	☐
_____	☐	☐	☐	☐	☐	☐	☐

DAILY Shit To Do

8 SATURDAY

WATER INTAKE: ○○○○○○○

9 SUNDAY

WATER INTAKE: ○○○○○○○

10 MONDAY

WATER INTAKE: ○○○○○○○

11 TUESDAY

WATER INTAKE: ○○○○○○○

12 WEDNESDAY

WATER INTAKE: ○○○○○○○

13 THURSDAY

WATER INTAKE: ○○○○○○○

14 FRIDAY

WATER INTAKE: ○○○○○○○

Notes

Tracker

			M	T	W	TH	F	S	SU

DAILY *Shit To Do*

15 | SATURDAY

WATER INTAKE: ○○○○○○○

16 | SUNDAY

WATER INTAKE: ○○○○○○○

17 | MONDAY

WATER INTAKE: ○○○○○○○

18 | TUESDAY

WATER INTAKE: ○○○○○○○

19 | WEDNESDAY

WATER INTAKE: ○○○○○○○

20 | THURSDAY

WATER INTAKE: ○○○○○○○

21 | FRIDAY

WATER INTAKE: ○○○○○○○

Notes

Tracker

	M	T	W	TH	F	S	SU
	☐	☐	☐	☐	☐	☐	☐
	☐	☐	☐	☐	☐	☐	☐
	☐	☐	☐	☐	☐	☐	☐
	☐	☐	☐	☐	☐	☐	☐

DAILY Shit To Do

22 SATURDAY

WATER INTAKE: ○○○○○○○

23 SUNDAY

WATER INTAKE: ○○○○○○○

24 MONDAY

WATER INTAKE: ○○○○○○○

25 TUESDAY

WATER INTAKE: ○○○○○○○

26 WEDNESDAY

WATER INTAKE: ○○○○○○○

27 THURSDAY

WATER INTAKE: ○○○○○○○

28 FRIDAY

WATER INTAKE: ○○○○○○○

Notes

Tracker

	M	T	W	TH	F	S	SU

DAILY Shit To Do

29 SATURDAY	30 SUNDAY	31 MONDAY	Notes
_____	_____	_____	_____
_____	_____	_____	_____
_____	_____	_____	_____
_____	_____	_____	_____
_____	_____	_____	_____
_____	_____	_____	_____
_____	_____	_____	_____
_____	_____	_____	_____
_____	_____	_____	_____
_____	_____	_____	_____
_____	_____	_____	_____
_____	_____	_____	_____
WATER INTAKE: ○○○○○○○	WATER INTAKE: ○○○○○○○	WATER INTAKE: ○○○○○○○	

Tracker

	M	T	W	TH	F	S	SU
_____	☐	☐	☐	☐	☐	☐	☐
_____	☐	☐	☐	☐	☐	☐	☐
_____	☐	☐	☐	☐	☐	☐	☐
_____	☐	☐	☐	☐	☐	☐	☐

MONTHLY Check-in

	1	2	3	4	5	6	7	8	9	10
FAMILY RELATIONSHIPS										
SOCIAL RELATIONSHIPS										
PERSONAL GROWTH										
ROMANTIC RELATIONSHIPS										
WORK/CAREER										
FINANCIAL										
HEALTH/FITNESS										
OVERALL										

1 = Sucked Ass   10 = Fucking Awesome

August

2023

Monthly Goals

Monthly Snapshot

Top Priorities

TASKS & NOTES

Monthly Wellness Goals

MIND
MY HOBBIES, LEARNING, READING, ETC.

BODY
MY EATING HABITS, EXERCISE, ETC.

SPIRIT
MY PURPOSE & MOTIVATION

ACTION STEPS TO TAKE TO MEET THESE GOALS:

Mind	Body	Spirit

Shit (that kills my joy) to avoid this month:

Shit To Get Done This Month

TO-DO / PROJECT	DUE DATE

Monthly Checklist

(CLEANING TASKS, HOME SERVICES TASKS LIKE
TERMITE OR PEST CONTROL, WORK TASKS, ETC.)

TASKS	MON	TUE	WED	THU	FRI	SAT	SUN
	○	○	○	○	○	○	○
	○	○	○	○	○	○	○
	○	○	○	○	○	○	○
	○	○	○	○	○	○	○
	○	○	○	○	○	○	○
	○	○	○	○	○	○	○
	○	○	○	○	○	○	○
	○	○	○	○	○	○	○
	○	○	○	○	○	○	○
	○	○	○	○	○	○	○
	○	○	○	○	○	○	○
	○	○	○	○	○	○	○
	○	○	○	○	○	○	○
	○	○	○	○	○	○	○
	○	○	○	○	○	○	○
	○	○	○	○	○	○	○
	○	○	○	○	○	○	○
	○	○	○	○	○	○	○
	○	○	○	○	○	○	○
	○	○	○	○	○	○	○
	○	○	○	○	○	○	○
	○	○	○	○	○	○	○
	○	○	○	○	○	○	○
	○	○	○	○	○	○	○
	○	○	○	○	○	○	○
	○	○	○	○	○	○	○
	○	○	○	○	○	○	○
	○	○	○	○	○	○	○
	○	○	○	○	○	○	○
	○	○	○	○	○	○	○

August

THIS MONTH'S GOALS:

ACTION LIST:
- ◯ _____
- ◯ _____
- ◯ _____
- ◯ _____
- ◯ _____
- ◯ _____
- ◯ _____
- ◯ _____
- ◯ _____

NOTES:

SUN	MON	TUES
30	31	1
6	7	8
13	14	15
20	21	22
27	28	29

SHIT TO DO THIS MONTH:

WED	THURS	FRI	SAT
2	3	4	5
9	10	11	12
16	17	18	19
23	24	25	26
30	31		

September

S	M	T	W	T	F	S
					1	2
3	4	5	6	7	8	9
10	11	12	13	14	15	16
17	18	19	20	21	22	23
24	25	26	27	28	29	30

...in loving memory of
when I gave a shit

DAILY Shit To Do

1 TUESDAY
_____
_____
_____
_____
_____
_____
_____
_____
_____
_____
_____
_____
_____
_____
WATER INTAKE: ○○○○○○○

2 WEDNESDAY
_____
_____
_____
_____
_____
_____
_____
_____
_____
_____
_____
_____
_____
_____
WATER INTAKE: ○○○○○○○

3 THURSDAY
_____
_____
_____
_____
_____
_____
_____
_____
_____
_____
_____
_____
_____
_____
WATER INTAKE: ○○○○○○○

4 FRIDAY
_____
_____
_____
_____
_____
_____
_____
_____
_____
_____
_____
_____
_____
_____
WATER INTAKE: ○○○○○○○

5 SATURDAY
_____
_____
_____
_____
_____
_____
_____
_____
_____
_____
_____
_____
_____
_____
_____
_____
WATER INTAKE: ○○○○○○○

6 SUNDAY
_____
_____
_____
_____
_____
_____
_____
_____
_____
_____
_____
_____
_____
_____
_____
_____
WATER INTAKE: ○○○○○○○

7 MONDAY
_____
_____
_____
_____
_____
_____
_____
_____
_____
_____
_____
_____
_____
_____
_____
_____
WATER INTAKE: ○○○○○○○

Notes
_____
_____
_____
_____
_____
_____
_____
_____
_____
_____
_____
_____
_____
_____
_____
_____
_____
_____
_____

Tracker

					M	T	W	TH	F	S	SU
_____					☐	☐	☐	☐	☐	☐	☐
_____					☐	☐	☐	☐	☐	☐	☐
_____					☐	☐	☐	☐	☐	☐	☐
_____					☐	☐	☐	☐	☐	☐	☐

DAILY Shit To Do

8 TUESDAY

WATER INTAKE: ⬡⬡⬡⬡⬡⬡⬡

9 WEDNESDAY

WATER INTAKE: ⬡⬡⬡⬡⬡⬡⬡

10 THURSDAY

WATER INTAKE: ⬡⬡⬡⬡⬡⬡⬡

11 FRIDAY

WATER INTAKE: ⬡⬡⬡⬡⬡⬡⬡

12 SATURDAY

WATER INTAKE: ⬡⬡⬡⬡⬡⬡⬡

13 SUNDAY

WATER INTAKE: ⬡⬡⬡⬡⬡⬡⬡

14 MONDAY

WATER INTAKE: ⬡⬡⬡⬡⬡⬡⬡

Notes

Tracker

	M	T	W	TH	F	S	SU

DAILY Shit To Do

15 **TUESDAY**
_____
_____
_____
_____
_____
_____
_____
_____
_____
_____
_____
_____
_____
_____
_____
_____
_____
_____
WATER INTAKE: ○○○○○○○

16 **WEDNESDAY**
_____
_____
_____
_____
_____
_____
_____
_____
_____
_____
_____
_____
_____
_____
_____
_____
_____
_____
WATER INTAKE: ○○○○○○○

17 **THURSDAY**
_____
_____
_____
_____
_____
_____
_____
_____
_____
_____
_____
_____
_____
_____
_____
_____
_____
_____
WATER INTAKE: ○○○○○○○

18 **FRIDAY**
_____
_____
_____
_____
_____
_____
_____
_____
_____
_____
_____
_____
_____
_____
_____
_____
_____
_____
WATER INTAKE: ○○○○○○○

19 **SATURDAY**
_____
_____
_____
_____
_____
_____
_____
_____
_____
_____
_____
_____
_____
_____
_____
_____
_____
_____
WATER INTAKE: ○○○○○○○

20 **SUNDAY**
_____
_____
_____
_____
_____
_____
_____
_____
_____
_____
_____
_____
_____
_____
_____
_____
_____
_____
WATER INTAKE: ○○○○○○○

21 **MONDAY**
_____
_____
_____
_____
_____
_____
_____
_____
_____
_____
_____
_____
_____
_____
_____
_____
_____
_____
WATER INTAKE: ○○○○○○○

Notes
_____
_____
_____
_____
_____
_____
_____
_____
_____
_____
_____
_____
_____
_____
_____
_____
_____
_____
_____
_____

Tracker

			M	T	W	TH	F	S	SU
_____			☐	☐	☐	☐	☐	☐	☐
_____			☐	☐	☐	☐	☐	☐	☐
_____			☐	☐	☐	☐	☐	☐	☐
_____			☐	☐	☐	☐	☐	☐	☐

DAILY Shit To Do

22 TUESDAY

WATER INTAKE: ○○○○○○○

23 WEDNESDAY

WATER INTAKE: ○○○○○○○

24 THURSDAY

WATER INTAKE: ○○○○○○○

25 FRIDAY

WATER INTAKE: ○○○○○○○

26 SATURDAY

WATER INTAKE: ○○○○○○○

27 SUNDAY

WATER INTAKE: ○○○○○○○

28 MONDAY

WATER INTAKE: ○○○○○○○

Notes

Tracker

	M	T	W	TH	F	S	SU

DAILY Shit To Do

29 TUESDAY	30 WEDNESDAY	31 THURSDAY	Notes
WATER INTAKE: ⬡⬡⬡⬡⬡⬡⬡	WATER INTAKE: ⬡⬡⬡⬡⬡⬡⬡	WATER INTAKE: ⬡⬡⬡⬡⬡⬡⬡	

Tracker

	M	T	W	TH	F	S	SU

MONTHLY Check-in

	1	2	3	4	5	6	7	8	9	10
FAMILY RELATIONSHIPS										
SOCIAL RELATIONSHIPS										
PERSONAL GROWTH										
ROMANTIC RELATIONSHIPS										
WORK/CAREER										
FINANCIAL										
HEALTH/FITNESS										
OVERALL										

1 = Sucked Ass   10 = Fucking Awesome

September
2023

Monthly Goals

Monthly Snapshot

Top Priorities

TASKS & NOTES

Monthly Wellness Goals

MIND
MY HOBBIES, LEARNING, READING, ETC.

BODY
MY EATING HABITS, EXERCISE, ETC.

SPIRIT
MY PURPOSE & MOTIVATION

ACTION STEPS TO TAKE TO MEET THESE GOALS:

Mind

Body

Spirit

Shit (that kills my joy) to avoid this month:

Shit To Get Done This Month

TO-DO / PROJECT	DUE DATE

Monthly Checklist

(CLEANING TASKS, HOME SERVICES TASKS LIKE
TERMITE OR PEST CONTROL, WORK TASKS, ETC.)

TASKS	MON	TUE	WED	THU	FRI	SAT	SUN
	○	○	○	○	○	○	○
	○	○	○	○	○	○	○
	○	○	○	○	○	○	○
	○	○	○	○	○	○	○
	○	○	○	○	○	○	○
	○	○	○	○	○	○	○
	○	○	○	○	○	○	○
	○	○	○	○	○	○	○
	○	○	○	○	○	○	○
	○	○	○	○	○	○	○
	○	○	○	○	○	○	○
	○	○	○	○	○	○	○
	○	○	○	○	○	○	○
	○	○	○	○	○	○	○
	○	○	○	○	○	○	○
	○	○	○	○	○	○	○
	○	○	○	○	○	○	○
	○	○	○	○	○	○	○
	○	○	○	○	○	○	○
	○	○	○	○	○	○	○
	○	○	○	○	○	○	○
	○	○	○	○	○	○	○
	○	○	○	○	○	○	○
	○	○	○	○	○	○	○
	○	○	○	○	○	○	○
	○	○	○	○	○	○	○
	○	○	○	○	○	○	○
	○	○	○	○	○	○	○
	○	○	○	○	○	○	○
	○	○	○	○	○	○	○

September

	SUN	MON	TUES
THIS MONTH'S GOALS:	27	28	29
	3	4	5
ACTION LIST:	10	11	12
	17	18	19
NOTES:	24	25	26

SHIT TO DO THIS MONTH:

WED	THURS	FRI	SAT
30	31	1	2
6	7	8	9
13	14	15	16
20	21	22	23
27	28	29	30

~ Let's keep the ~
DUMBFUCKERY
to a minimum today

October

S	M	T	W	T	F	S
1	2	3	4	5	6	7
8	9	10	11	12	13	14
15	16	17	18	19	20	21
22	23	24	25	26	27	28
29	30	31				

DAILY Shit To Do

1 FRIDAY

_____
_____
_____
_____
_____
_____
_____
_____
_____
_____
_____
_____
_____
_____
_____
_____
_____
_____

WATER INTAKE: ○○○○○○○

2 SATURDAY

_____
_____
_____
_____
_____
_____
_____
_____
_____
_____
_____
_____
_____
_____
_____
_____
_____
_____

WATER INTAKE: ○○○○○○○

3 SUNDAY

_____
_____
_____
_____
_____
_____
_____
_____
_____
_____
_____
_____
_____
_____
_____
_____
_____
_____

WATER INTAKE: ○○○○○○○

4 MONDAY

_____
_____
_____
_____
_____
_____
_____
_____
_____
_____
_____
_____
_____
_____
_____
_____
_____
_____

WATER INTAKE: ○○○○○○○

5 TUESDAY

_____
_____
_____
_____
_____
_____
_____
_____
_____
_____
_____
_____
_____
_____
_____
_____
_____
_____

WATER INTAKE: ○○○○○○○

6 WEDNESDAY

_____
_____
_____
_____
_____
_____
_____
_____
_____
_____
_____
_____
_____
_____
_____
_____
_____
_____

WATER INTAKE: ○○○○○○○

7 THURSDAY

_____
_____
_____
_____
_____
_____
_____
_____
_____
_____
_____
_____
_____
_____
_____
_____
_____
_____

WATER INTAKE: ○○○○○○○

Notes

_____
_____
_____
_____
_____
_____
_____
_____
_____
_____
_____
_____
_____
_____
_____
_____
_____
_____
_____
_____

Tracker

			M	T	W	TH	F	S	SU
_____			☐	☐	☐	☐	☐	☐	☐
_____			☐	☐	☐	☐	☐	☐	☐
_____			☐	☐	☐	☐	☐	☐	☐
_____			☐	☐	☐	☐	☐	☐	☐

DAILY *Shit To Do*

8 | FRIDAY
WATER INTAKE: ○○○○○○○

9 | SATURDAY
WATER INTAKE: ○○○○○○○

10 | SUNDAY
WATER INTAKE: ○○○○○○○

11 | MONDAY
WATER INTAKE: ○○○○○○○

12 | TUESDAY
WATER INTAKE: ○○○○○○○

13 | WEDNESDAY
WATER INTAKE: ○○○○○○○

14 | THURSDAY
WATER INTAKE: ○○○○○○○

Notes

Tracker

	M	T	W	TH	F	S	SU
	☐	☐	☐	☐	☐	☐	☐
	☐	☐	☐	☐	☐	☐	☐
	☐	☐	☐	☐	☐	☐	☐
	☐	☐	☐	☐	☐	☐	☐

DAILY Shit To Do

15 FRIDAY

WATER INTAKE: ○○○○○○○

16 SATURDAY

WATER INTAKE: ○○○○○○○

17 SUNDAY

WATER INTAKE: ○○○○○○○

18 MONDAY

WATER INTAKE: ○○○○○○○

19 TUESDAY

WATER INTAKE: ○○○○○○○

20 WEDNESDAY

WATER INTAKE: ○○○○○○○

21 THURSDAY

WATER INTAKE: ○○○○○○○

Notes

Tracker

	M	T	W	TH	F	S	SU

DAILY *Shit To Do*

22 FRIDAY	**23** SATURDAY	**24** SUNDAY	**25** MONDAY

WATER INTAKE: ○○○○○○○ WATER INTAKE: ○○○○○○○ WATER INTAKE: ○○○○○○○ WATER INTAKE: ○○○○○○○

26 TUESDAY	**27** WEDNESDAY	**28** THURSDAY	*Notes*

WATER INTAKE: ○○○○○○○ WATER INTAKE: ○○○○○○○ WATER INTAKE: ○○○○○○○

Tracker

		M	T	W	TH	F	S	SU
		☐	☐	☐	☐	☐	☐	☐
		☐	☐	☐	☐	☐	☐	☐
		☐	☐	☐	☐	☐	☐	☐
		☐	☐	☐	☐	☐	☐	☐

DAILY Shit To Do

29 FRIDAY	30 SATURDAY	Notes

WATER INTAKE: ⟡⟡⟡⟡⟡⟡⟡ WATER INTAKE: ⟡⟡⟡⟡⟡⟡⟡

Tracker

	M	T	W	TH	F	S	SU
	☐	☐	☐	☐	☐	☐	☐
	☐	☐	☐	☐	☐	☐	☐
	☐	☐	☐	☐	☐	☐	☐
	☐	☐	☐	☐	☐	☐	☐

MONTHLY Check-in

	1	2	3	4	5	6	7	8	9	10
FAMILY RELATIONSHIPS										
SOCIAL RELATIONSHIPS										
PERSONAL GROWTH										
ROMANTIC RELATIONSHIPS										
WORK/CAREER										
FINANCIAL										
HEALTH/FITNESS										
OVERALL										

1 = Sucked Ass   10 = Fucking Awesome

October

2023

Monthly Goals

Monthly Snapshot

Top Priorities

TASKS & NOTES

Monthly Wellness Goals

MIND
MY HOBBIES, LEARNING, READING, ETC.

BODY
MY EATING HABITS, EXERCISE, ETC.

SPIRIT
MY PURPOSE & MOTIVATION

ACTION STEPS TO TAKE TO MEET THESE GOALS:

Mind

Body

Spirit

Shit (that kills my joy) to avoid this month:

Shit To Get Done This Month

TO-DO / PROJECT	DUE DATE

Monthly Checklist

(CLEANING TASKS, HOME SERVICES TASKS LIKE
TERMITE OR PEST CONTROL, WORK TASKS, ETC.)

TASKS	MON	TUE	WED	THU	FRI	SAT	SUN
	○	○	○	○	○	○	○
	○	○	○	○	○	○	○
	○	○	○	○	○	○	○
	○	○	○	○	○	○	○
	○	○	○	○	○	○	○
	○	○	○	○	○	○	○
	○	○	○	○	○	○	○
	○	○	○	○	○	○	○
	○	○	○	○	○	○	○
	○	○	○	○	○	○	○
	○	○	○	○	○	○	○
	○	○	○	○	○	○	○
	○	○	○	○	○	○	○
	○	○	○	○	○	○	○
	○	○	○	○	○	○	○
	○	○	○	○	○	○	○
	○	○	○	○	○	○	○
	○	○	○	○	○	○	○
	○	○	○	○	○	○	○
	○	○	○	○	○	○	○
	○	○	○	○	○	○	○
	○	○	○	○	○	○	○
	○	○	○	○	○	○	○
	○	○	○	○	○	○	○
	○	○	○	○	○	○	○
	○	○	○	○	○	○	○
	○	○	○	○	○	○	○
	○	○	○	○	○	○	○
	○	○	○	○	○	○	○
	○	○	○	○	○	○	○

October

	SUN	MON	TUES
	1	2	3
	8	9	10
	15	16	17
	22	23	24
	29	30	31

THIS MONTH'S GOALS:

ACTION LIST:
- ○ _____
- ○ _____
- ○ _____
- ○ _____
- ○ _____
- ○ _____
- ○ _____
- ○ _____
- ○ _____

NOTES:

SHIT TO DO THIS MONTH:

WED	THURS	FRI	SAT
4	5	6	7
11	12	13	14
18	19	20	21
25	26	27	28

November

S	M	T	W	T	F	S
			1	2	3	4
5	6	7	8	9	10	11
12	13	14	15	16	17	18
19	20	21	22	23	24	25
26	27	28	29	30		

I've come to the point in my life where I need a stronger word than FUCK

DAILY Shit To Do

1 SUNDAY

_____
_____
_____
_____
_____
_____
_____
_____
_____
_____
_____
_____
_____
_____

WATER
INTAKE: ⬡⬡⬡⬡⬡⬡⬡

2 MONDAY

_____
_____
_____
_____
_____
_____
_____
_____
_____
_____
_____
_____
_____
_____

WATER
INTAKE: ⬡⬡⬡⬡⬡⬡⬡

3 TUESDAY

_____
_____
_____
_____
_____
_____
_____
_____
_____
_____
_____
_____
_____
_____

WATER
INTAKE: ⬡⬡⬡⬡⬡⬡⬡

4 WEDNESDAY

_____
_____
_____
_____
_____
_____
_____
_____
_____
_____
_____
_____
_____
_____

WATER
INTAKE: ⬡⬡⬡⬡⬡⬡⬡

5 THURSDAY

_____
_____
_____
_____
_____
_____
_____
_____
_____
_____
_____
_____
_____
_____

WATER
INTAKE: ⬡⬡⬡⬡⬡⬡⬡

6 FRIDAY

_____
_____
_____
_____
_____
_____
_____
_____
_____
_____
_____
_____
_____
_____

WATER
INTAKE: ⬡⬡⬡⬡⬡⬡⬡

7 SATURDAY

_____
_____
_____
_____
_____
_____
_____
_____
_____
_____
_____
_____
_____
_____

WATER
INTAKE: ⬡⬡⬡⬡⬡⬡⬡

Notes

_____
_____
_____
_____
_____
_____
_____
_____
_____
_____
_____
_____
_____
_____

Tracker

		M	T	W	TH	F	S	SU
_____		☐	☐	☐	☐	☐	☐	☐
_____		☐	☐	☐	☐	☐	☐	☐
_____		☐	☐	☐	☐	☐	☐	☐
_____		☐	☐	☐	☐	☐	☐	☐

DAILY Shit To Do

| 8 SUNDAY | 9 MONDAY | 10 TUESDAY | 11 WEDNESDAY |

WATER INTAKE: ⬡⬡⬡⬡⬡⬡⬡   WATER INTAKE: ⬡⬡⬡⬡⬡⬡⬡   WATER INTAKE: ⬡⬡⬡⬡⬡⬡⬡   WATER INTAKE: ⬡⬡⬡⬡⬡⬡⬡

| 12 THURSDAY | 13 FRIDAY | 14 SATURDAY | Notes |

WATER INTAKE: ⬡⬡⬡⬡⬡⬡⬡   WATER INTAKE: ⬡⬡⬡⬡⬡⬡⬡   WATER INTAKE: ⬡⬡⬡⬡⬡⬡⬡

Tracker

	M	T	W	TH	F	S	SU
	☐	☐	☐	☐	☐	☐	☐
	☐	☐	☐	☐	☐	☐	☐
	☐	☐	☐	☐	☐	☐	☐
	☐	☐	☐	☐	☐	☐	☐

DAILY Shit To Do

15 **SUNDAY**

WATER INTAKE: ○○○○○○○

16 **MONDAY**

WATER INTAKE: ○○○○○○○

17 **TUESDAY**

WATER INTAKE: ○○○○○○○

18 **WEDNESDAY**

WATER INTAKE: ○○○○○○○

19 **THURSDAY**

WATER INTAKE: ○○○○○○○

20 **FRIDAY**

WATER INTAKE: ○○○○○○○

21 **SATURDAY**

WATER INTAKE: ○○○○○○○

Notes

Tracker

	M	T	W	TH	F	S	SU

DAILY *Shit To Do*

22 SUNDAY

WATER INTAKE:

23 MONDAY

WATER INTAKE:

24 TUESDAY

WATER INTAKE:

25 WEDNESDAY

WATER INTAKE:

26 THURSDAY

WATER INTAKE:

27 FRIDAY

WATER INTAKE:

28 SATURDAY

WATER INTAKE:

Notes

Tracker

		M	T	W	TH	F	S	SU

DAILY Shit To Do

29 SUNDAY

_____
_____
_____
_____
_____
_____
_____
_____
_____
_____
_____
_____
_____
_____
_____
_____
_____
_____
_____

WATER INTAKE: ○○○○○○○

30 MONDAY

_____
_____
_____
_____
_____
_____
_____
_____
_____
_____
_____
_____
_____
_____
_____
_____
_____
_____
_____

WATER INTAKE: ○○○○○○○

31 TUESDAY

_____
_____
_____
_____
_____
_____
_____
_____
_____
_____
_____
_____
_____
_____
_____
_____
_____
_____
_____

WATER INTAKE: ○○○○○○○

Notes

_____
_____
_____
_____
_____
_____
_____
_____
_____
_____
_____
_____
_____
_____
_____
_____
_____
_____
_____
_____
_____

Tracker

		M	T	W	TH	F	S	SU
_____								
_____								
_____								
_____								

MONTHLY Check-in

	1	2	3	4	5	6	7	8	9	10
FAMILY RELATIONSHIPS										
SOCIAL RELATIONSHIPS										
PERSONAL GROWTH										
ROMANTIC RELATIONSHIPS										
WORK/CAREER										
FINANCIAL										
HEALTH/FITNESS										
OVERALL										

1 = Sucked Ass   10 = Fucking Awesome

November

November

2023

Monthly Goals

Monthly Snapshot

Top Priorities

TASKS & NOTES

Monthly Wellness Goals

MIND	BODY	SPIRIT
MY HOBBIES, LEARNING, READING, ETC.	MY EATING HABITS, EXERCISE, ETC.	MY PURPOSE & MOTIVATION

ACTION STEPS TO TAKE TO MEET THESE GOALS:

Mind	Body	Spirit

Shit (that kills my joy) to avoid this month:

Shit To Get Done This Month

TO-DO / PROJECT	DUE DATE

Monthly Checklist

(CLEANING TASKS, HOME SERVICES TASKS LIKE
TERMITE OR PEST CONTROL, WORK TASKS, ETC.)

TASKS	MON	TUE	WED	THU	FRI	SAT	SUN
	○	○	○	○	○	○	○
	○	○	○	○	○	○	○
	○	○	○	○	○	○	○
	○	○	○	○	○	○	○
	○	○	○	○	○	○	○
	○	○	○	○	○	○	○
	○	○	○	○	○	○	○
	○	○	○	○	○	○	○
	○	○	○	○	○	○	○
	○	○	○	○	○	○	○
	○	○	○	○	○	○	○
	○	○	○	○	○	○	○
	○	○	○	○	○	○	○
	○	○	○	○	○	○	○
	○	○	○	○	○	○	○
	○	○	○	○	○	○	○
	○	○	○	○	○	○	○
	○	○	○	○	○	○	○
	○	○	○	○	○	○	○
	○	○	○	○	○	○	○
	○	○	○	○	○	○	○
	○	○	○	○	○	○	○
	○	○	○	○	○	○	○
	○	○	○	○	○	○	○
	○	○	○	○	○	○	○
	○	○	○	○	○	○	○
	○	○	○	○	○	○	○
	○	○	○	○	○	○	○
	○	○	○	○	○	○	○
	○	○	○	○	○	○	○

November

SUN	MON	TUES
29	30	31
5	6	7
12	13	14
19	20	21
26	27	28

THIS MONTH'S GOALS:

ACTION LIST:
- ○
- ○
- ○
- ○
- ○
- ○
- ○
- ○
- ○

NOTES:

SHIT TO DO THIS MONTH:

WED	THURS	FRI	SAT
1	2	3	4
8	9	10	11
15	16	17	18
22	23	24	25
29	30		

December

S	M	T	W	T	F	S
					1	2
3	4	5	6	7	8	9
10	11	12	13	14	15	16
17	18	19	20	21	22	23
24	25	26	27	28	29	30
31						

**DIDN'T CARE YESTERDAY.
DON'T GIVE A SHIT TODAY.**
Probably won't give a fuck tomorrow.

DAILY Shit To Do

1 WEDNESDAY

_____
_____
_____
_____
_____
_____
_____
_____
_____
_____
_____
_____
_____

WATER INTAKE: ○○○○○○○

2 THURSDAY

_____
_____
_____
_____
_____
_____
_____
_____
_____
_____
_____
_____
_____

WATER INTAKE: ○○○○○○○

3 FRIDAY

_____
_____
_____
_____
_____
_____
_____
_____
_____
_____
_____
_____
_____

WATER INTAKE: ○○○○○○○

4 SATURDAY

_____
_____
_____
_____
_____
_____
_____
_____
_____
_____
_____
_____
_____

WATER INTAKE: ○○○○○○○

5 SUNDAY

_____
_____
_____
_____
_____
_____
_____
_____
_____
_____
_____
_____
_____

WATER INTAKE: ○○○○○○○

6 MONDAY

_____
_____
_____
_____
_____
_____
_____
_____
_____
_____
_____
_____
_____

WATER INTAKE: ○○○○○○○

7 TUESDAY

_____
_____
_____
_____
_____
_____
_____
_____
_____
_____
_____
_____
_____

WATER INTAKE: ○○○○○○○

Notes

_____
_____
_____
_____
_____
_____
_____
_____
_____
_____
_____
_____
_____
_____

Tracker

	M	T	W	TH	F	S	SU
_____	☐	☐	☐	☐	☐	☐	☐
_____	☐	☐	☐	☐	☐	☐	☐
_____	☐	☐	☐	☐	☐	☐	☐
_____	☐	☐	☐	☐	☐	☐	☐

DAILY *Shit To Do*

8 | **WEDNESDAY**

WATER INTAKE: ○○○○○○○

9 | **THURSDAY**

WATER INTAKE: ○○○○○○○

10 | **FRIDAY**

WATER INTAKE: ○○○○○○○

11 | **SATURDAY**

WATER INTAKE: ○○○○○○○

12 | **SUNDAY**

WATER INTAKE: ○○○○○○○

13 | **MONDAY**

WATER INTAKE: ○○○○○○○

14 | **TUESDAY**

WATER INTAKE: ○○○○○○○

Notes

Tracker

	M	T	W	TH	F	S	SU
	☐	☐	☐	☐	☐	☐	☐
	☐	☐	☐	☐	☐	☐	☐
	☐	☐	☐	☐	☐	☐	☐
	☐	☐	☐	☐	☐	☐	☐

DAILY *Shit To Do*

15 **WEDNESDAY**	16 **THURSDAY**	17 **FRIDAY**	18 **SATURDAY**

WATER INTAKE: ○○○○○○○ ○○○○○○○ ○○○○○○○ ○○○○○○○

19 **SUNDAY**	20 **MONDAY**	21 **TUESDAY**	*Notes*

WATER INTAKE: ○○○○○○○ ○○○○○○○ ○○○○○○○

Tracker

	M	T	W	TH	F	S	SU
	☐	☐	☐	☐	☐	☐	☐
	☐	☐	☐	☐	☐	☐	☐
	☐	☐	☐	☐	☐	☐	☐
	☐	☐	☐	☐	☐	☐	☐

DAILY *Shit To Do*

22 WEDNESDAY

WATER
INTAKE: ○○○○○○○

23 THURSDAY

WATER
INTAKE: ○○○○○○○

24 FRIDAY

WATER
INTAKE: ○○○○○○○

25 SATURDAY

WATER
INTAKE: ○○○○○○○

26 SUNDAY

WATER
INTAKE: ○○○○○○○

27 MONDAY

WATER
INTAKE: ○○○○○○○

28 TUESDAY

WATER
INTAKE: ○○○○○○○

Notes

Tracker

	M	T	W	TH	F	S	SU

DAILY Shit To Do

29 | WEDNESDAY

_____
_____
_____
_____
_____
_____
_____
_____
_____
_____
_____
_____
_____
_____
_____
_____

WATER INTAKE: ⬡⬡⬡⬡⬡⬡⬡

30 | THURSDAY

_____
_____
_____
_____
_____
_____
_____
_____
_____
_____
_____
_____
_____
_____
_____
_____

WATER INTAKE: ⬡⬡⬡⬡⬡⬡⬡

Notes

_____
_____
_____
_____
_____
_____
_____
_____
_____
_____
_____
_____
_____
_____
_____

Tracker

	M	T	W	TH	F	S	SU
_____							
_____							
_____							
_____							

MONTHLY Check-in

	1	2	3	4	5	6	7	8	9	10
FAMILY RELATIONSHIPS										
SOCIAL RELATIONSHIPS										
PERSONAL GROWTH										
ROMANTIC RELATIONSHIPS										
WORK/CAREER										
FINANCIAL										
HEALTH/FITNESS										
OVERALL										

1 = Sucked Ass   10 = Fucking Awesome

December
2023

Monthly Goals

Monthly Snapshot

Top Priorities

TASKS & NOTES

Monthly Wellness Goals

MIND
MY HOBBIES, LEARNING,
READING, ETC.

BODY
MY EATING HABITS,
EXERCISE, ETC.

SPIRIT
MY PURPOSE
& MOTIVATION

ACTION STEPS TO TAKE TO MEET THESE GOALS:

Mind

Body

Spirit

Shit (that kills my joy) to avoid this month:

Shit To Get Done This Month

TO-DO / PROJECT	DUE DATE

Monthly Checklist

(CLEANING TASKS, HOME SERVICES TASKS LIKE
TERMITE OR PEST CONTROL, WORK TASKS, ETC.)

TASKS	MON	TUE	WED	THU	FRI	SAT	SUN
	○	○	○	○	○	○	○
	○	○	○	○	○	○	○
	○	○	○	○	○	○	○
	○	○	○	○	○	○	○
	○	○	○	○	○	○	○
	○	○	○	○	○	○	○
	○	○	○	○	○	○	○
	○	○	○	○	○	○	○
	○	○	○	○	○	○	○
	○	○	○	○	○	○	○
	○	○	○	○	○	○	○
	○	○	○	○	○	○	○
	○	○	○	○	○	○	○
	○	○	○	○	○	○	○
	○	○	○	○	○	○	○
	○	○	○	○	○	○	○
	○	○	○	○	○	○	○
	○	○	○	○	○	○	○
	○	○	○	○	○	○	○
	○	○	○	○	○	○	○
	○	○	○	○	○	○	○
	○	○	○	○	○	○	○
	○	○	○	○	○	○	○
	○	○	○	○	○	○	○
	○	○	○	○	○	○	○
	○	○	○	○	○	○	○
	○	○	○	○	○	○	○
	○	○	○	○	○	○	○
	○	○	○	○	○	○	○
	○	○	○	○	○	○	○

December

	SUN	MON	TUES
	26	27	28
	3	4	5
	10	11	12
	17	18	19
	24	25	26
	31	SHIT TO DO THIS MONTH:	

THIS MONTH'S GOALS:

ACTION LIST:
- ○ _____
- ○ _____
- ○ _____
- ○ _____
- ○ _____
- ○ _____
- ○ _____
- ○ _____
- ○ _____

NOTES:

WED	THURS	FRI	SAT
29	30	1	2
6	7	8	9
13	14	15	16
20	21	22	23
27	28	29	30

MAKE EACH DAY YOUR
fucking masterpiece

DAILY *Shit To Do*

1 **FRIDAY**

WATER INTAKE: ○○○○○○○

2 **SATURDAY**

WATER INTAKE: ○○○○○○○

3 **SUNDAY**

WATER INTAKE: ○○○○○○○

4 **MONDAY**

WATER INTAKE: ○○○○○○○

5 **TUESDAY**

WATER INTAKE: ○○○○○○○

6 **WEDNESDAY**

WATER INTAKE: ○○○○○○○

7 **THURSDAY**

WATER INTAKE: ○○○○○○○

Notes

Tracker

	M	T	W	TH	F	S	SU

DAILY Shit To Do

8 FRIDAY

WATER INTAKE: ⬡⬡⬡⬡⬡⬡⬡⬡

9 SATURDAY

WATER INTAKE: ⬡⬡⬡⬡⬡⬡⬡⬡

10 SUNDAY

WATER INTAKE: ⬡⬡⬡⬡⬡⬡⬡⬡

11 MONDAY

WATER INTAKE: ⬡⬡⬡⬡⬡⬡⬡⬡

12 TUESDAY

WATER INTAKE: ⬡⬡⬡⬡⬡⬡⬡⬡

13 WEDNESDAY

WATER INTAKE: ⬡⬡⬡⬡⬡⬡⬡⬡

14 THURSDAY

WATER INTAKE: ⬡⬡⬡⬡⬡⬡⬡⬡

Notes

Tracker

		M	T	W	TH	F	S	SU
		☐	☐	☐	☐	☐	☐	☐
		☐	☐	☐	☐	☐	☐	☐
		☐	☐	☐	☐	☐	☐	☐
		☐	☐	☐	☐	☐	☐	☐

DAILY Shit To Do

15 FRIDAY

WATER INTAKE: ○○○○○○○

16 SATURDAY

WATER INTAKE: ○○○○○○○

17 SUNDAY

WATER INTAKE: ○○○○○○○

18 MONDAY

WATER INTAKE: ○○○○○○○

19 TUESDAY

WATER INTAKE: ○○○○○○○

20 WEDNESDAY

WATER INTAKE: ○○○○○○○

21 THURSDAY

WATER INTAKE: ○○○○○○○

Notes

Tracker

	M	T	W	TH	F	S	SU

DAILY Shit To Do

22 FRIDAY

WATER INTAKE: ⬡⬡⬡⬡⬡⬡⬡⬡

23 SATURDAY

WATER INTAKE: ⬡⬡⬡⬡⬡⬡⬡⬡

24 SUNDAY

WATER INTAKE: ⬡⬡⬡⬡⬡⬡⬡⬡

25 MONDAY

WATER INTAKE: ⬡⬡⬡⬡⬡⬡⬡⬡

26 TUESDAY

WATER INTAKE: ⬡⬡⬡⬡⬡⬡⬡⬡

27 WEDNESDAY

WATER INTAKE: ⬡⬡⬡⬡⬡⬡⬡⬡

28 THURSDAY

WATER INTAKE: ⬡⬡⬡⬡⬡⬡⬡⬡

Notes

Tracker

	M	T	W	TH	F	S	SU

DAILY Shit To Do

29 FRIDAY	30 SATURDAY	31 SUNDAY	Notes
_____	_____	_____	_____
_____	_____	_____	_____
_____	_____	_____	_____
_____	_____	_____	_____
_____	_____	_____	_____
_____	_____	_____	_____
_____	_____	_____	_____
_____	_____	_____	_____
_____	_____	_____	_____
_____	_____	_____	_____
_____	_____	_____	_____
_____	_____	_____	_____
WATER INTAKE: ○○○○○○○	WATER INTAKE: ○○○○○○○	WATER INTAKE: ○○○○○○○	

Tracker

	M	T	W	TH	F	S	SU
_____	☐	☐	☐	☐	☐	☐	☐
_____	☐	☐	☐	☐	☐	☐	☐
_____	☐	☐	☐	☐	☐	☐	☐
_____	☐	☐	☐	☐	☐	☐	☐

MONTHLY Check-in

	1	2	3	4	5	6	7	8	9	10
FAMILY RELATIONSHIPS										
SOCIAL RELATIONSHIPS										
PERSONAL GROWTH										
ROMANTIC RELATIONSHIPS										
WORK/CAREER										
FINANCIAL										
HEALTH/FITNESS										
OVERALL										

1 = Sucked Ass   10 = Fucking Awesome

Made in the USA
Monee, IL
03 December 2022

19285764R00083